CGP has Year 1 Phonics sounded out!

CGP's Targeted Practice Books are packed with fun and friendly activities to build Year 1 pupils' confidence as they learn to read and write.

What's more, they follow the National Curriculum 'Letters and Sounds' programme, so you can be sure they cover everything children need to learn.

This is **Year 1 Targeted Practice Book 3**. It covers the final section of **Phase 5** of the 'Letters and Sounds' programme, including:

- Alternative ways of spelling the sounds:
  "f", "e", "ow", "j", "ear", "s", "air", "igh", "oa", "ee", "sh"
- Reading and writing **tricky words**

What CGP is all about

Our sole aim here at CGP is to produce the highest quality books
— carefully written, immaculately presented and
dangerously close to being funny.

Then we work our socks off to get them out to you
— at the cheapest possible prices.

How to Use this Book

In this Book

You'll meet...

 Word Birds: they'll help you read and write words and sentences

 Chatty Bats: they'll tell your helper what words to say in writing activities

 Jolly Jugglers: they'll help you practise those tricky words

Hints for Helpers

Here are a few things to bear in mind when using this book:

- CGP's Phonics series aligns with **Letters and Sounds**, the Department for Education's systematic synthetic phonics programme. Reception books 1-5 covered Phases 1, 2, 3 and 4. The first two Year 1 books centred on the first two sections of Phase 5. This book concentrates on the final section of Phase 5 and focuses on alternative ways of spelling sounds.

- The book should be worked through **in order**, as new content builds on content covered earlier in the book.

- The central aims of this book are to draw attention to the common ways to spell sounds and to develop an awareness and understanding of spelling choices.
  Many of the activities suggest that you, the helper, read the words and sentences. This allows children to focus exclusively on listening for and identifying target sounds, before looking at the ways in which that sound can be written.

- '**Tricky words**' are words with letters that have a sound that does not correspond to the expected sound, or that have a sound that has not yet been learned. These words need to be practised until they can be read straight away without blending sounds.

- '**Word frames**' are used on Writing Tricky Words pages. Word frames for words that can be sounded out have boxes. There is one box for each sound.

- This resource requires children to match images to words. You may need to help children to **identify** some images they're not sure of.

Above all, promote a **positive, confident attitude** towards reading and writing by giving lots of praise and encouragement.

Contents

Written by Karen Bryant-Mole

Editors: Christopher Lindle, Sam Mann, Sam Norman
Reviewers: Ross Knaggs, Stef Lake, Clare Leck
With thanks to Holly Robinson and Lucy Towle for the proofreading.
ISBN: 978 1 78908 018 6

Images throughout the book from www.edu-clips.com
Printed by Elanders Ltd, Newcastle upon Tyne.
Based on the classic CGP style created by Richard Parsons.

Year 1 Book 2 Check

There's more than one way to say the sound of some letters.
Put a **tick** (✓) below each word you can say correctly.

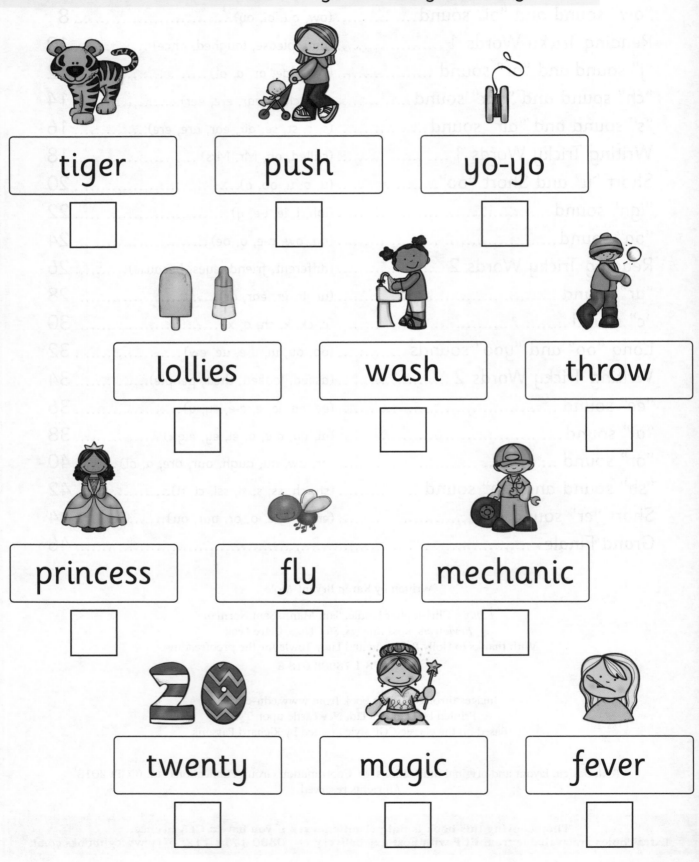

tiger

push

yo-yo

lollies

wash

throw

princess

fly

mechanic

twenty

magic

fever

Read the words under each picture. **Circle** the correct word.

| beetle | gnome | kneel |
| apple | thumb | wrist |

If you can read the tricky word on the block, **circle** it.

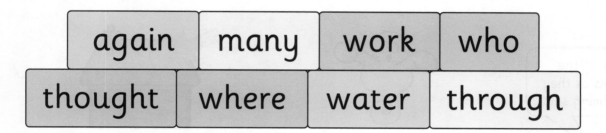

again | many | work | who
thought | where | water | through

Listen to the tricky words these bats are saying.
Write each word in one of the special word frames.

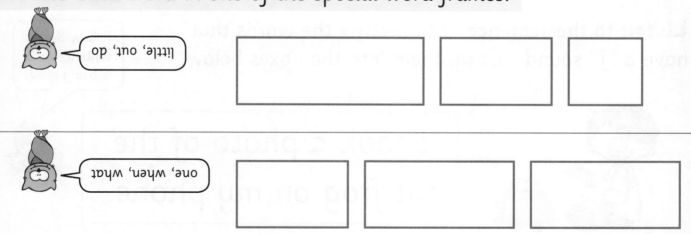

little, out, do

one, when, what

I can remember everything I learned in Book 2.

Phonics — Year 1 Book 3

"f" sound and "e" sound

Listen to these words: **flag**, **dolphin**.
There's a "f" sound in both words.

Look at the two different ways the "f" sound is written.

flag

dolphin

Listen to the words. **Circle** the letters that have a "f" sound.

Look at the words as they are being said.

phantom

roof

Listen to the sentence. **Underline** the words that have a "f" sound. **Copy** them into the boxes below.

Follow the sentence as it is being read.

I took a photo of the fat frog on my phone.

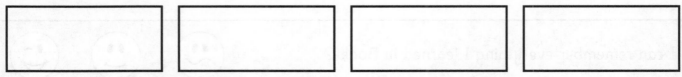

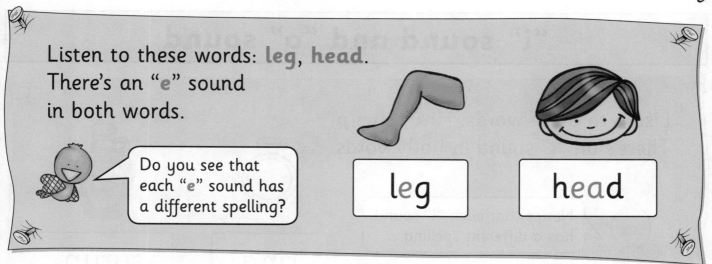

Listen to these words: leg, head.
There's an "e" sound in both words.

Do you see that each "e" sound has a different spelling?

leg

head

Listen to the words. Circle the letters that have an "e" sound.

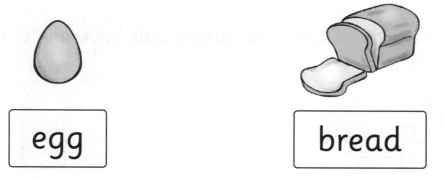

egg

bread

Listen to the sentences. Underline the words that have an "e" sound. Copy them into the boxes below.

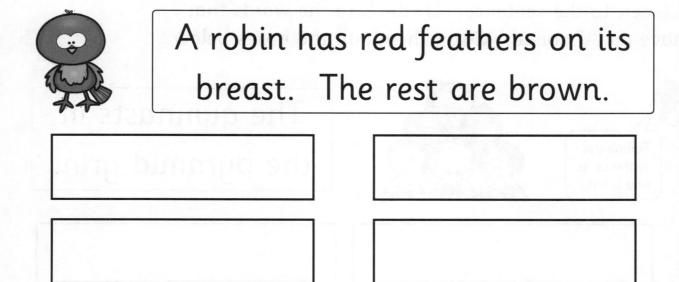

A robin has red feathers on its breast. The rest are brown.

I know the common ways to spell the "f" sound and the "e" sound.

"i" sound and "o" sound

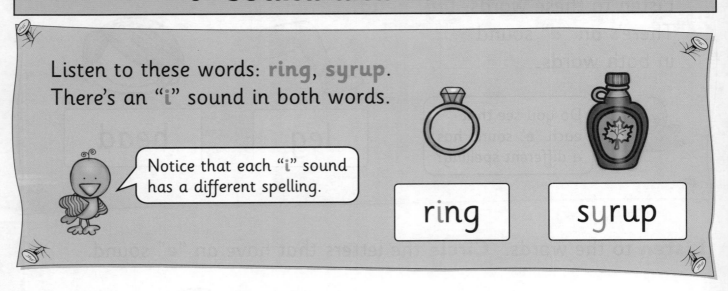

Listen to these words: ring, syrup.
There's an "i" sound in both words.

Notice that each "i" sound has a different spelling.

ring   syrup

Listen to the words. **Circle** the letters that have an "i" sound.

symbols   milk

Listen to the sentence. **Underline** the words that have an "i" sound. **Copy** them into the boxes below.

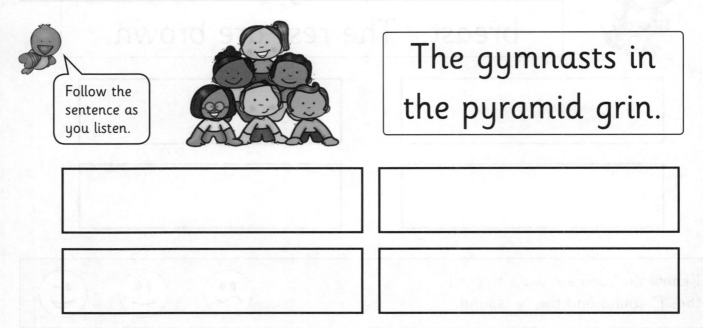

Follow the sentence as you listen.

The gymnasts in the pyramid grin.

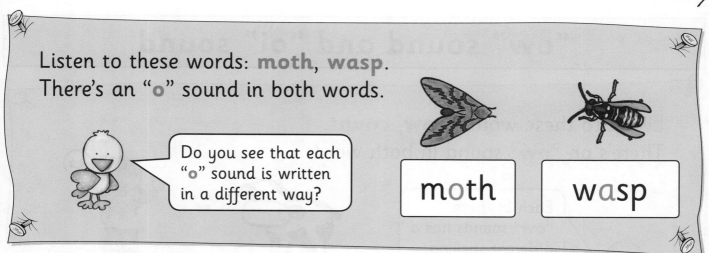

Listen to these words: **moth**, **wasp**.
There's an "**o**" sound in both words.

Do you see that each "**o**" sound is written in a different way?

moth   wasp

Listen to the words. **Circle** the letters that have an "**o**" sound.

clock   wand

Listen to the sentence. **Underline** the words that have an "**o**" sound. **Copy** them into the boxes below.

If we wander to the pond, we might spot some swans.

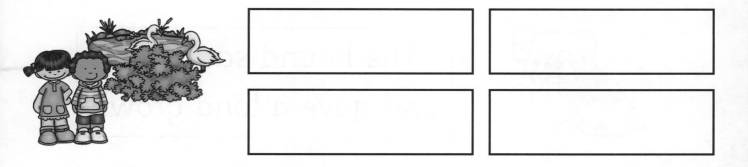

I know the common ways to spell the "i" sound and the "o" sound.

Phonics — Year 1 Book 3

"ow" sound and "oi" sound

Listen to these words: cow, count.
There's an "ow" sound in both words.

Each of these "ow" sounds has a different spelling.

cow

count

Listen to the words. **Circle** the letters that have an "ow" sound.

clown

cloud

Listen to the sentence. **Underline** the words that have an "ow" sound. **Copy** them into the boxes below.

The hound sat down and gave a loud growl.

Listen to these words: **boil**, **toy**.
There's an "**oi**" sound in both words.

Look at the two different ways the "**oi**" sound is written.

boil   toy

Listen to the words. **Circle** the letters that have an "**oi**" sound.

oyster   foil

Listen to the sentence. **Underline** the words that have an "**oi**" sound. **Copy** them into the boxes below.

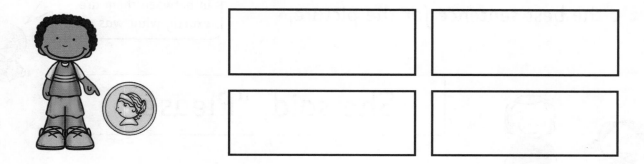

The boy points at the royal head on the coin.

I know the common ways to spell the "ow" sound and the "oi" sound.

Reading Tricky Words 1

Let's learn some more tricky words.
These tricky words are any, please, laughed and once.

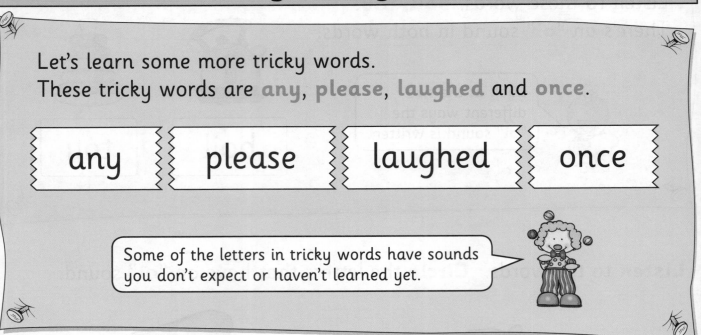

| any | please | laughed | once |

Some of the letters in tricky words have sounds you don't expect or haven't learned yet.

Read each caption. **Match** it to the best picture.

many apples

hardly any apples

Those special marks tell you that the words in between them are exactly what was said.

Look at the picture. **Read** the sentences.
Circle the best sentence for the picture.

She said, "Please."

She said, "Thank you."

Read the sentences. **Match** each sentence to the correct picture.

Tess laughed to herself.

Come here at once, Bob.

Al did not need any help.

Read the sentences. **Circle** the best picture for the sentences.

Once, I met a clown. I laughed at her jokes.
I said, "Do you have any more jokes, please?"

I can read the tricky words 'any', 'please', 'laughed' and 'once'. I know that special marks show spoken words.

"j" sound and "ar" sound

Listen to these words: jeep, germ, fridge.
There's a "j" sound in every word.

Do you see that each "j" sound has a different spelling?

jeep

germ

fridge

Listen to the words. Circle the letters that have a "j" sound.

gem

bridge

jacket

Listen to the sentence. Underline the words that
have a "j" sound. Copy them into the boxes below.

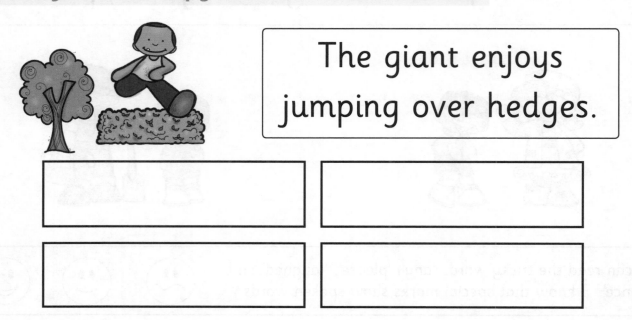

The giant enjoys
jumping over hedges.

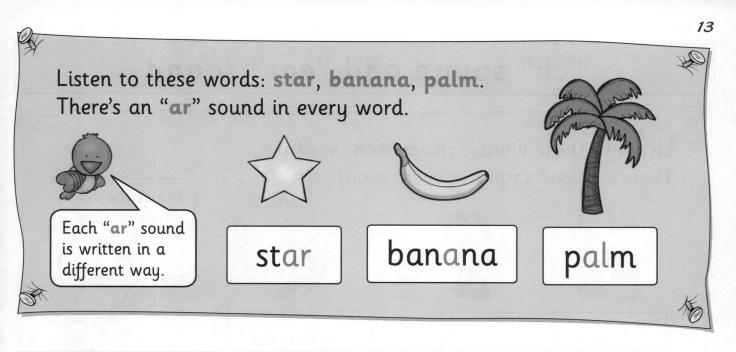

Listen to these words: star, banana, palm.
There's an "ar" sound in every word.

Each "ar" sound is written in a different way.

star   banana   palm

Listen to the words. Circle the letters that have an "ar" sound.

half   tomato   card

Listen to the sentence. Underline the words that have an "ar" sound. Copy them into the boxes below.

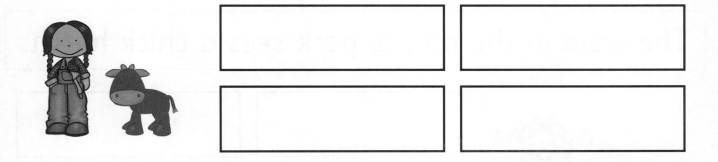

The farmer was rather fond of her dark calf.

I know the common ways to spell the "j" sound and the "ar" sound.

"ch" sound and "ear" sound

Listen to these words: chop, itch, vulture.
There's a "ch" sound in every word.

Notice the different ways the "ch" sound is written.

chop   itch   vulture

Listen to the words. **Circle** the letters that have a "ch" sound.

bench   ketchup   capture

Listen to the sentence. **Underline** the words that have a "ch" sound. **Copy** them into the boxes below.

The child in the nature park sees a chick hatch.

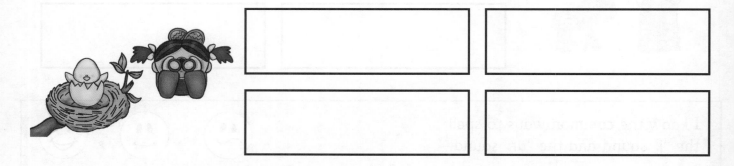

Listen to these words: **beard**, **sphere**, **cheer**.
There's an "**ear**" sound in every word.

Each "**ear**" sound is written in a different way.

beard   sphere   cheer

Listen to the words. **Circle** the letters that have an "**ear**" sound.

steer   severe   spear

Listen to the sentence.   **Underline** the words that have an "**ear**" sound. **Copy** them into the boxes below.

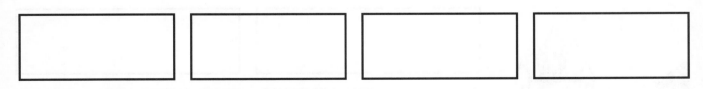

The deer are near, so stay here until it's clear.

I know the common ways to spell the "ch" sound and the "ear" sound.

Phonics — Year 1 Book 3

"s" sound and "air" sound

Listen to these words:
sip, celery, whistle, house.
There's a "s" sound in every word.

Each "s" sound has a different spelling.

| sip | celery | whistle | house |

Listen to the words. **Circle** the letters that have a "s" sound.

| listen | city | mouse | desk |

Listen to the sentence. **Underline** the words that have a "s" sound. **Copy** them into the boxes below.

The curse makes the castle turn to ice.

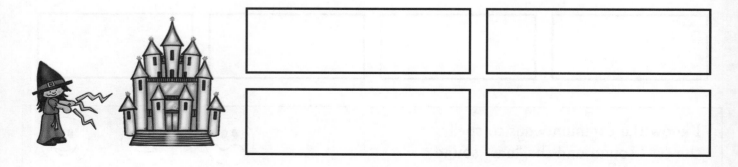

Listen to these words: fair, tear, square, everywhere.
There's an "air" sound in every word.

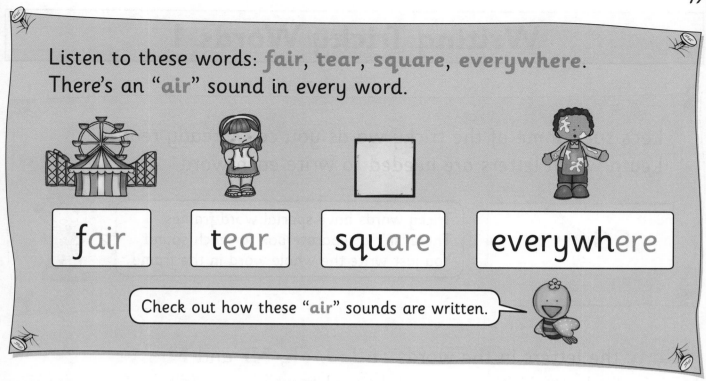

fair   tear   square   everywhere

Check out how these "air" sounds are written.

Listen to the words. Circle the letters that have an "air" sound.

pear   there   chair   scare

Listen to the sentence.
Underline the words that have an "air" sound.
Copy them into the boxes below.

Where are the bears that share this lair?

I know the common ways to spell
the "s" sound and the "air" sound.

Writing Tricky Words 1

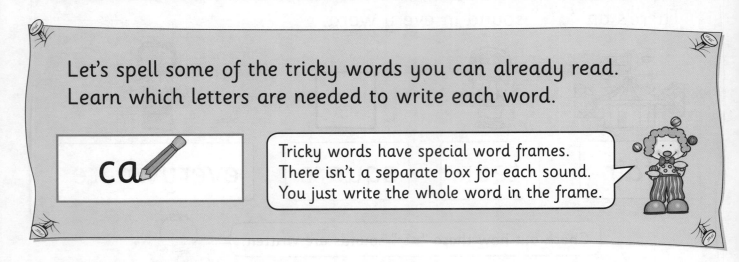

Let's spell some of the tricky words you can already read.
Learn which letters are needed to write each word.

ca

Tricky words have special word frames.
There isn't a separate box for each sound.
You just write the whole word in the frame.

Name the letters in the words **called**, **oh**, **Mr** and **Mrs**.
Copy the letters into the special word frames.

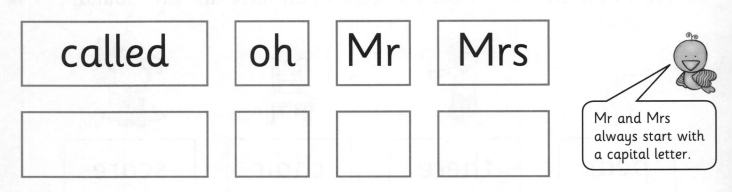

called	oh	Mr	Mrs

Mr and Mrs always start with a capital letter.

Listen carefully to the sentence the bat is saying.
Write the sentence in the word frames.

Mrs Bond got a hat.

Surnames always start with a capital letter, too.

Find out more about Mrs Bond's hat, and about someone else.
Listen to the sentences the bats are saying, then **write** them.

Oh. It is too big.

Put a full stop after the first word, then start a new sentence.

The sound at the end of 'too' has two **o**s.

Mr West has a pet.

I wonder what its name is?

It is called Spot.

Remember that pets' names also start with a capital letter.

I can write sentences that include the tricky words 'called', 'oh', 'Mr' and 'Mrs'.

Phonics — Year 1 Book 3

Short "u" and Short "oo"

Not everyone uses the short "u" sound. If you say the words **hut** and **bush** with the same sound in the middle, go straight to the page opposite.

Listen to these words: **hut**, **money**.
There's a short "u"
sound in both words.

Each short "u" sound has a different spelling.

hut money

Listen to the words. **Circle** the letters that have a short "u" sound.

brothers

drum

Listen to the sentence. **Underline** the words that have a short "u" sound. **Copy** them into the boxes below.

The monkey hung upside down in front of me.

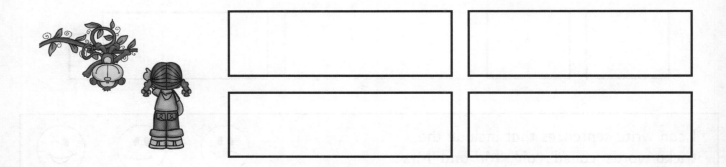

Not everyone uses the short "oo" sound in the same words!
How you spell this sound depends on the words you say it in.

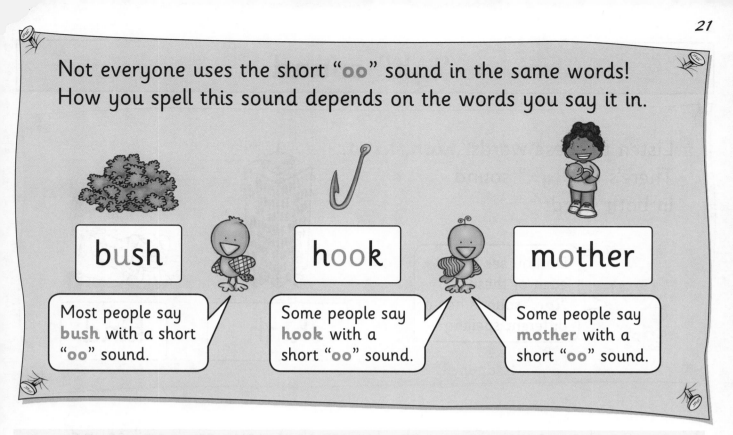

bush

Most people say **bush** with a short "oo" sound.

hook

Some people say **hook** with a short "oo" sound.

mother

Some people say **mother** with a short "oo" sound.

Listen then **repeat**. **Circle** words <u>you</u> say with a short "oo" sound.

foot

bull

oven

Listen then **repeat**. **Underline** words <u>you</u> say with a short "oo" sound. **Copy** them into the boxes below.

That jar full of honey looks good!

You may not need all the boxes.

I know the common ways to spell the short "u" sound and the short "oo" sound in words where I say these sounds.

"igh" sound

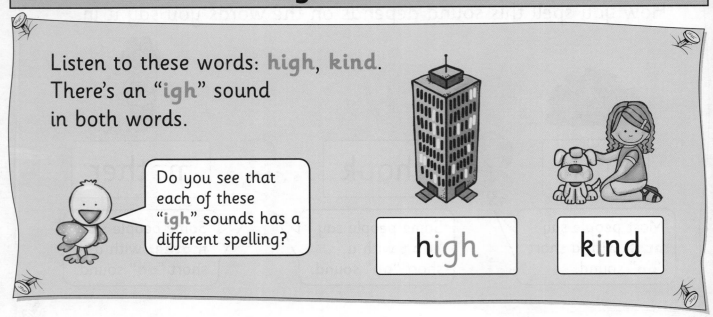

Listen to these words: **high**, **kind**.
There's an "**igh**" sound
in both words.

Do you see that each of these "**igh**" sounds has a different spelling?

high   kind

Listen to the words. **Circle** the letters that have an "**igh**" sound.

behind   right

Listen to the sentence. **Underline** the words that have an "**igh**" sound. **Copy** them into the boxes below.

The sight of the spider gave the child a fright.

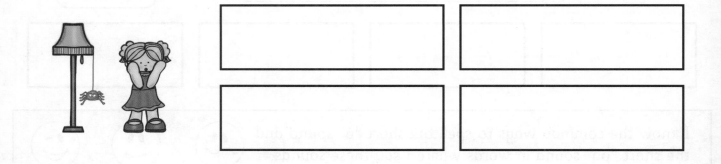

Listen to these words: **tie**, **smile**, **shy**.
There's an "**igh**" sound in each of these words, too.

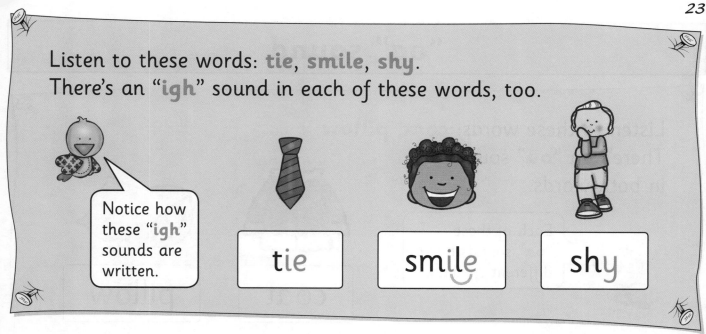

Notice how these "**igh**" sounds are written.

tie   smile   shy

Listen to the words. **Circle** the letters that have an "**igh**" sound.

cry   spies   slide

Listen to the sentence. **Underline** the words that have an "**igh**" sound. **Copy** them into the boxes below.

Come and try some of my fine apple pie.

I know the common ways to spell the "igh" sound.

Phonics — Year 1 Book 3

"oa" sound

Listen to these words: coat, pillow.
There's an "oa" sound
in both words.

Each of these "oa" sounds has a different spelling.

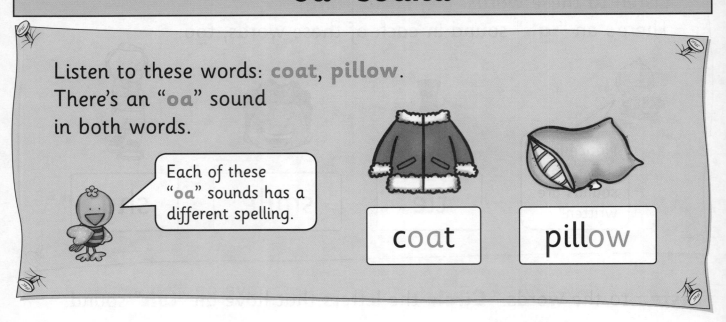

coat pillow

Listen to the words. **Circle** the letters that have an "oa" sound.

window   toast

Listen to the sentence. **Underline** the words that have an "oa" sound. **Copy** them into the boxes below.

I know that a foal will not grow up to be a goat.

Listen to these words: rope, gecko, doe.
There's an "oa" sound in each of these words, too.

Look at the different ways the "oa" sound is written.

rope   gecko   doe

Listen to the words. Circle the letters that have an "oa" sound.

goes   hippo   cone

Listen to the sentence. Underline the words that have an "oa" sound. Copy them into the boxes below.

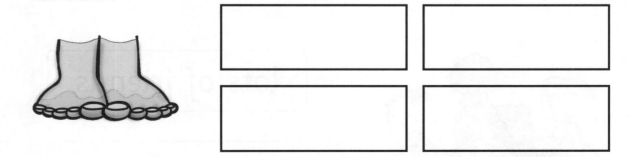

It was so cold his toes froze!

I know the common ways to spell the "oa" sound.

Reading Tricky Words 2

Let's learn some new tricky words.
These tricky words are different, eyes, because and friend.

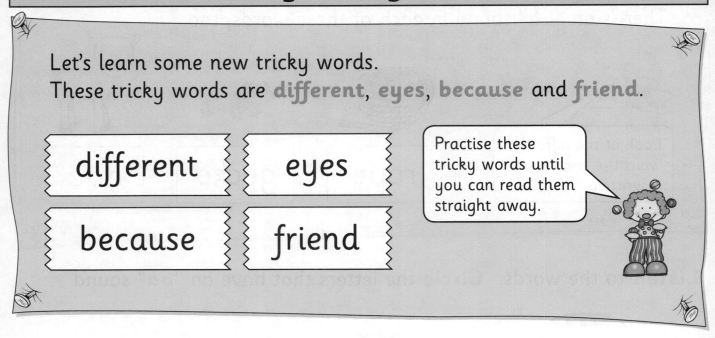

different

eyes

because

friend

Practise these tricky words until you can read them straight away.

Read each caption. **Match** it to the correct picture.

the same

different

Look at the picture. **Read** the captions.
Circle the correct caption for the picture.

It's nice to have friends!

lots of friends

no friends

Read the sentences. Match each sentence to the correct picture.

You can open your eyes.

I jog because it's fun.

Jeb made a new friend.

Read the sentence. Circle the best picture for the sentence.

My friend and I are different because she has blue eyes and mine are brown.

I can read the tricky words 'different', 'eyes', 'because' and 'friend'.

"ur" sound

Listen to these words: curl, bird, iceberg.
There's an "ur" sound in every word.

Each "ur" sound is written in a different way.

| curl | bird | iceberg |

Listen to the words. **Circle** the letters that have an "ur" sound.

| shirt | fern | surf |

Listen to the sentence. **Underline** the words that have an "ur" sound. **Copy** them into the boxes below.

The girl in the green skirt hurt her leg.

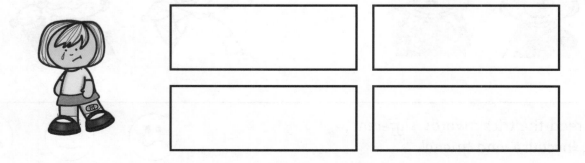

Listen to these words: search, work.
There's an "ur" sound in both
of these words, too.

Look at the different ways these "ur" sounds are written.

search

work

Listen to the words. **Circle** the letters that have an "ur" sound.

worm

learn

Listen to the sentence. **Underline** the words that have an "ur" sound. **Copy** them into the boxes below.

I heard that the biggest pearl
in the world is worth a lot.

I know the common ways to spell the "ur" sound.

"c" sound

Listen to these words: car, duck, kite.
There's a "c" sound in every word.

Notice that each "c" sound is written in a different way.

car   duck   kite

Listen to the words. **Circle** the letters that have a "c" sound.

skip   cap   ticket

Listen to the sentence. **Underline** the words that have a "c" sound. **Copy** them into the boxes below.

My black cat likes to play with the pink wool.

Listen to these words: ache, quiz, fox.
There's a "c" sound in each of these words, too.

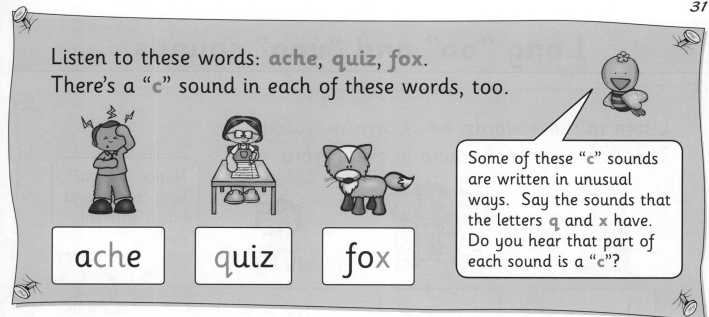

Some of these "c" sounds are written in unusual ways. Say the sounds that the letters q and x have. Do you hear that part of each sound is a "c"?

ache   quiz   fox

Listen to the words. **Circle** the letters that have a "c" sound.

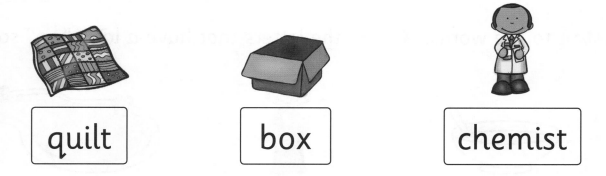

quilt   box   chemist

Listen to the sentence. **Underline** the words that have a "c" sound. **Copy** them into the boxes below.

Next, the queen will visit six schools.

I know the common ways to spell the "c" sound.

Long "oo" and "yoo" sounds

Listen to these words: **boot**, **group**, **juicy**.
There's a long "**oo**" sound in every word.

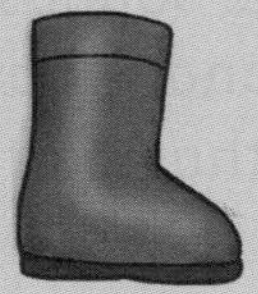

Notice that each long "**oo**" sound has a different spelling.

boot | group | juicy

Listen to the words. **Circle** the letters that have a long "**oo**" sound.

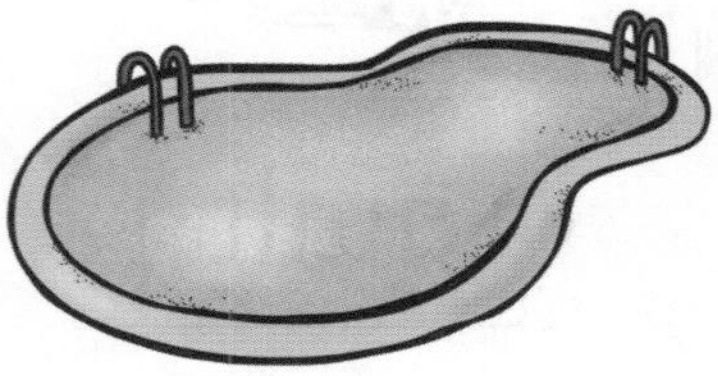

soup | suit | pool

Listen to the sentence. **Underline** the words that have a long "**oo**" sound. **Copy** them into the boxes below.

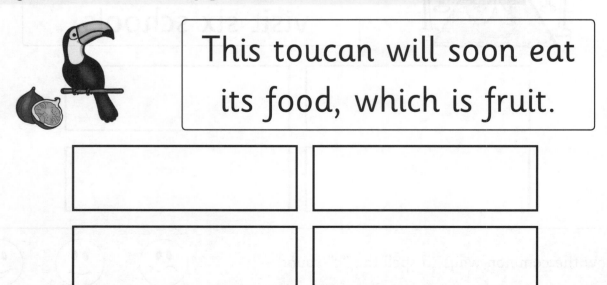

This toucan will soon eat its food, which is fruit.

Listen to these words: **flute**, **glue**, **screw**.

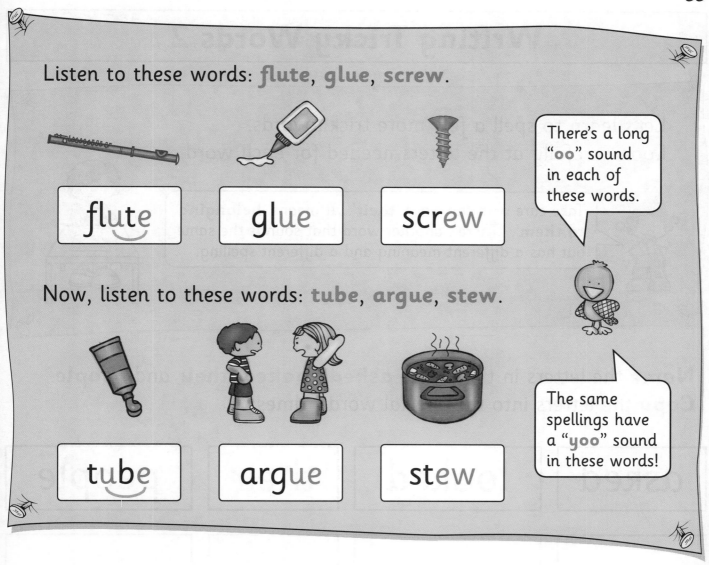

fl**u**te   gl**ue**   scr**ew**

There's a long "**oo**" sound in each of these words.

Now, listen to these words: **tube**, **argue**, **stew**.

t**u**be   arg**ue**   st**ew**

The same spellings have a "**yoo**" sound in these words!

Listen to the sentences. **Underline** the words that have an "**oo**" or "**yoo**" sound. **Copy** them into the boxes below.

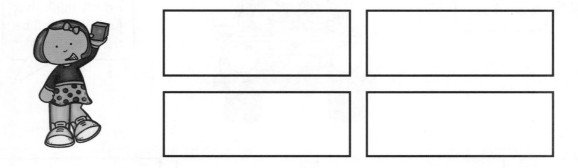

She threw the blue cube. How rude!

I know the common ways to spell the long "**oo**" and "**yoo**" sounds.

Writing Tricky Words 2

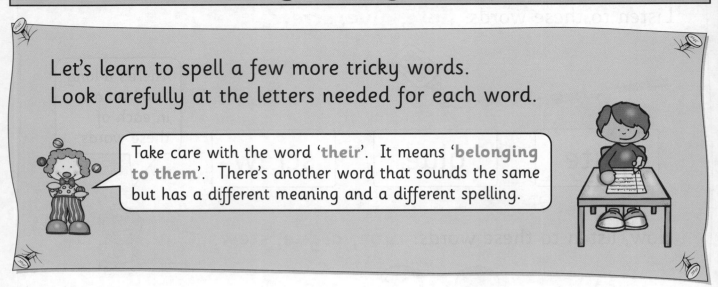

Let's learn to spell a few more tricky words.
Look carefully at the letters needed for each word.

Take care with the word 'their'. It means 'belonging to them'. There's another word that sounds the same but has a different meaning and a different spelling.

Name the letters in the words **asked**, **looked**, **their** and **people**.
Copy the letters into the special word frames.

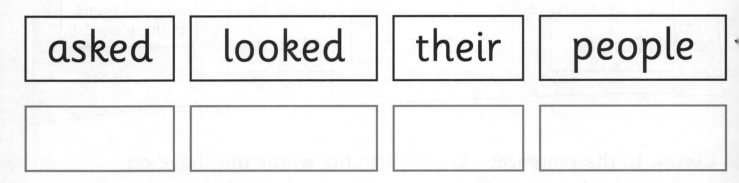

| asked | looked | their | people |

Listen carefully to the sentence the bat is saying.
Write the sentence in the word frames.

The people got lost.

I don't think that first word will be tricky for you!

Find out what happens next!
Listen to the sentences the bats are saying, then **write** them.

Their map was old.

There's another tricky word in there that you already know.

They asked the way.

The last sound of the last word has two letters.

They looked so glad.

In this sentence there's one more tricky word that you already know!

I can write sentences that include the tricky words 'asked', 'looked', 'their' and 'people'.

"ee" sound

Listen to these words:
feet, **bead**, **thief**, **secret**.
There's an "ee" sound in every word.

Each "ee" sound is written in a different way.

feet   bead   thief   secret

Listen to the words. **Circle** the letters that have an "ee" sound.

cookie   me   leaf   tree

Listen to the sentence. **Underline** the words that have an "ee" sound. **Copy** them into the boxes below.

My dog needs to be on a lead in this field.

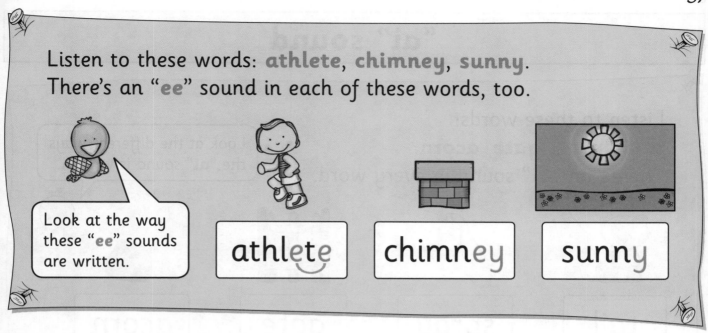

Listen to these words: **athlete**, **chimney**, **sunny**.
There's an "**ee**" sound in each of these words, too.

Look at the way these "**ee**" sounds are written.

athlete   chimney   sunny

Listen to the words. **Circle** the letters that have an "**ee**" sound.

trolley   jelly   trapeze

Listen to the sentence. **Underline** the words that have an "**ee**" sound. **Copy** them into the boxes below.

These rusty keys look very old.

I know the common ways to spell the "ee" sound.

"ai" sound

Listen to these words:
tail, spray, gate, acorn.
There's an "ai" sound in every word.

Look at the different ways the "ai" sound is written.

| tail | spray | gate | acorn |

Listen to the words. **Circle** the letters that have an "ai" sound.

| tray | snake | train | potato |

Listen to the sentence. **Underline** the words that have an "ai" sound. **Copy** them into the boxes below.

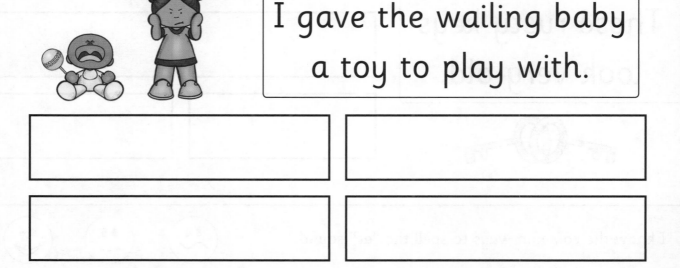

I gave the wailing baby a toy to play with.

Listen to these words: veil, grey, neigh.
There's an "ai" sound in each of these words, too.

Check out how these "ai" sounds are written.

veil   grey   neigh

Listen to the words. Circle the letters that have an "ai" sound.

weigh   reins   disobey

Listen to the sentences. Underline the words that have an "ai" sound. Copy them into the boxes below.

There are eight reindeer.
They are pulling a sleigh.

I know the common ways to spell the "ai" sound.

"or" sound

Listen to these words:
torch, straw, haunted, taught.
There's an "or" sound in every word.

Each "or" sound has a different spelling.

| torch | straw | haunted | taught |

Listen to the words. Circle the letters that have an "or" sound.

| seesaw | fork | launch | naughty |

Listen to the sentence. Underline the words that have an "or" sound. Copy them into the boxes below.

Paul got caught in an awful storm.

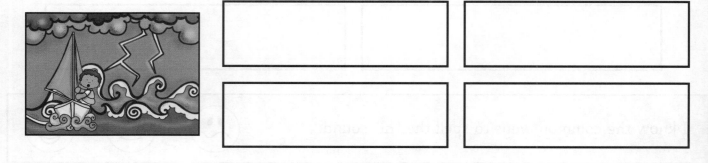

Listen to these words: **court**, **snore**, **bald**, **stalk**.
There's an "**or**" sound in
each of these words, too.

Look at how these "**or**"
sounds are written.

| court | snore | bald | stalk |

Listen to the words. **Circle** the letters that have an "**or**" sound.

| chalk | core | pour | water |

Listen to the sentence. **Underline** the words that
have an "**or**" sound. **Copy** them into the boxes below.

Four more cats walk
along the wall.

I know most of the common ways to spell the "**or**" sound.

Phonics — Year 1 Book 3

"sh" sound and "zh" sound

Listen to these words:
ship, chute, tissue, sure.
There's a "sh" sound in every word.

Every "sh" sound is written in a different way.

| ship | chute | tissue | sure |

Listen to the sentence. **Underline** the words that have a "sh" sound. **Copy** them into the boxes below.

I assure you the chef did not put sugar on the fish.

Sometimes the letter **s** has a soft "zh" sound instead of a "sh" sound.
Say this word using a "zh" sound. **Circle** the correct picture.

treasure

Listen to these words: **mansion**, **discussion**, **musician**, **patient**. There's a "sh" sound in each of these words, too.

> Notice the different ways the "sh" sound is written.

| mansion | discussion | musician | patient |

Sometimes the letters **s** and **i** have a soft "zh" sound instead of a "sh" sound. **Say** this word using a "zh" sound. **Circle** the correct picture.

collision

Listen to the sentence. **Underline** the words that have a "sh" sound or a "zh" sound. **Copy** them into the boxes below.

I have a vision of a special mission to the space station.

I know the common ways to spell the "sh" sound.
I know that sometimes 's' and 'si' have a "zh" sound.

© CGP — Not to be photocopied

Phonics — Year 1 Book 3

Short "er" sound

Listen to these words:
letter, **circus**, **afraid**, **kitten**.
There's a short "**er**" sound in every word.

Look at the different ways the short "**er**" sound is written.

| letter | circus | afraid | kitten |

Listen to the words. **Circle** the letters that have a short "**er**" sound.

| cactus | ladder | children | asleep |

Listen to the sentence. **Underline** the words that have a short "**er**" sound. **Copy** them into the boxes below.

This sudden tantrum
was all about his dinner.

Listen to these words: **melon**, **mirror**, **colour**, **enormous**.
There's a short "**er**" sound
in each of these words, too.

Each of the short "**er**" sounds below has a different spelling.

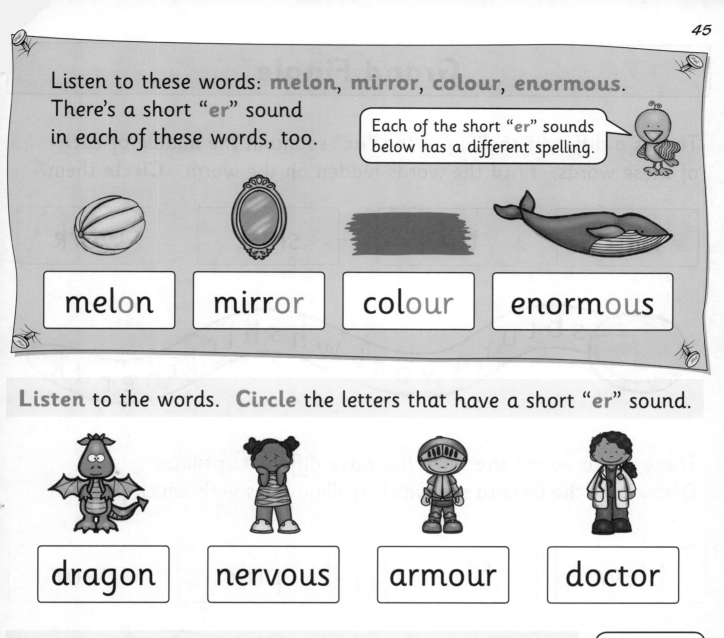

| melon | mirror | colour | enormous |

Listen to the words. **Circle** the letters that have a short "**er**" sound.

dragon | nervous | armour | doctor

Listen to the sentence. **Underline** the words that have a short "**er**" sound. **Copy** them into the boxes below.

Savour is another word for **enjoy**.

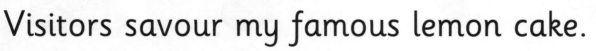

Visitors savour my famous lemon cake.

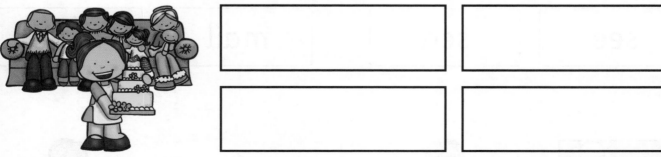

I know some of the common ways
to spell the short "**er**" sound.

Phonics — Year 1 Book 3

Grand Finale

There's a different spelling of the "ur" sound in the middle of each of these words. **Find** the words hidden on the worm. **Circle** them.

herd	turn	shirt	work

s b t u r n w o r k w h s h i r t i h e r d k

These words sound the same but have different spellings!
Draw over the lines to see which spelling goes with which picture.

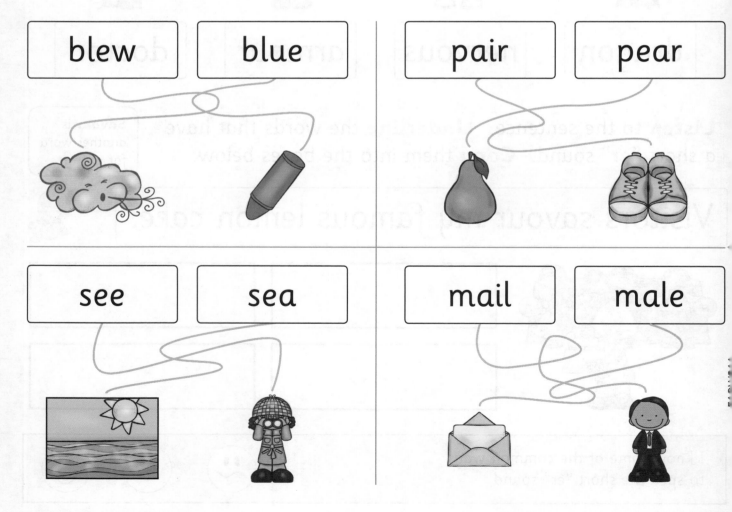

blew	blue

pair	pear

see	sea

mail	male